Gold Star

Spelling

hutch

boy

blue

PaRragon

Bath · New York · Cologne · Melbourne · Delhi
Hong Kong · Shenzhen · Singapore

Helping your child

⭐ The activities in this book will help your child to learn how to spell a variety of common words including colours, numbers, days of the week and plurals.

⭐ Children learn to spell by reading and writing. If your child finds a word difficult to spell, try to follow this method:

LOOK at the word; COVER UP the word; WRITE the word; CHECK the word.

⭐ It is important that you set aside time to do the activities together. Your child does not need to complete each page in one go. Do a little at a time and give lots of encouragement and praise.

⭐ The answers to the activities are on page 32.

⭐ Remember that the gold stars are a reward for effort as well as for achievement.

Written by Betty Root and Nina Filipek
Educational Consultant: Martin Malcolm
Illustrated by Simon Abbot

This edition published by Parragon Books Ltd in 2016

Parragon Books Ltd
Chartist House
15-17 Trim Street
Bath BA1 1HA, UK
www.parragon.com

ISBN 978-1-4748-5010-0

Printed in China

Contents

First letter sounds

Choose one letter to make each word.

a	b	c	d	e	f	g	h

_gg

_nt

_ap

_og

_oat

_en

_ox

_ish

Copy the words in alphabetical order from a to h.

1. a _____

2. b _____

3. c _____

4. _____

5. _____

6. _____

7. _____

8. _____

Look at the pictures. Can you spot something that begins with each letter?

| i | j | k | l | m | n | o | p | q | r |

Fill in the gaps.

The __ing and __ueen had lots of pets.

They had a __ion, a __onkey and a __ig.

They had an __wl in a __est.

They had a __abbit with big ears.

They fed them all on __elly and __ce cream.

Put the words you made in alphabetical order, from i to r.

1. i _____   2. j _____

3. k _____   4. l _____

5. m _____   6. n _____

7. o _____   8. p _____

9. q _____   10. r _____

Note for parent: This activity focuses on alphabetical order. Remind your child that words are
ordered alphabetically in dictionaries and other reference materials.

5

Choose one letter to make each word.

| s | t | u | v | w | x | y | z |

_ap

_an

_asp

_ellow

_ip

_mbrella

_-ray

_un

Copy the words in alphabetical order from s to z.

1. s _____

2. t _____

3. u _____

4. v _____

5. w _____

6. _____

7. _____

8. _____

Note for parent: This activity focuses on alphabetical order. Remind your child that words are ordered alphabetically in dictionaries and other reference materials.

Middle sounds

Write the missing letter to finish each word. Read the words.

 d__g

 c__p

 p__g

 b__t

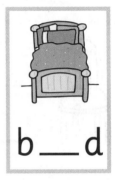 b__d

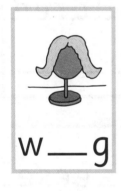 w__g

 c__t

 f__x

 w__b

 d__ck

 n__t

 s__n

 r__t

 b__s

Note for parent: This activity focuses on the vowel sounds that are missing in each word. Remind your child that the vowels are: **a**, **e**, **i**, **o** and **u**.

7

First write **ch** to make each word. LOOK at the word. COVER it up. WRITE it on the line below. CHECK if you are right!

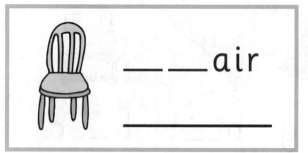 ___ air
_____

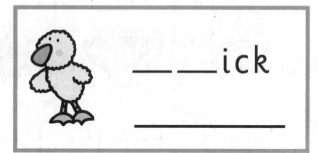 ___ ick
_____

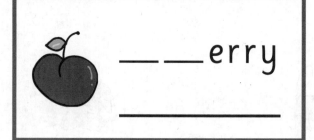 ___ erry
_____

 ___ ildren
_____

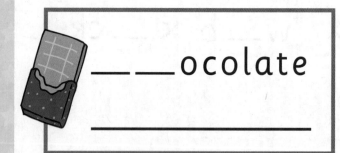 ___ ocolate
_____

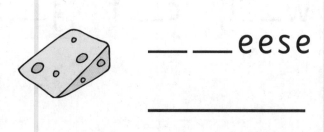 ___ eese
_____

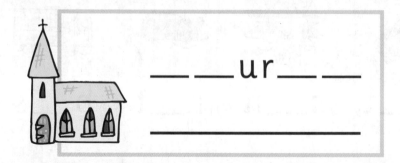 ___ ur ___
_____

Note for parent: Remind your child to practise the LOOK, COVER, WRITE, CHECK method to spell other words in this book.

Wordsearch for **sh**

Look in the grid for words that begin or end with **sh**. Circle them, then copy each word next to the right picture.

s	h	a	r	k	n	b
h	m	f	o	d	e	r
e	d	i	s	h	s	u
e	h	s	r	u	l	s
p	s	h	e	d	o	h

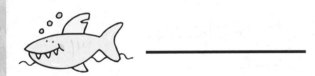 _____

 _____

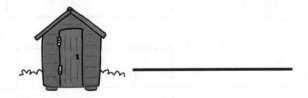 _____

 _____

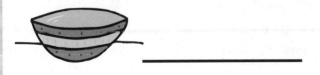 _____

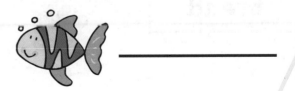 _____

Note for parent: Ask your child to try to spell these and other words containing the **sh** sound. For example: shop, shell, dash, wish.

br sound

Write **br** in the gaps to make these words.
Read them out.

___ain	___anch
___oom	___idle
___ook	___ing
___im	___eeze
___onze	___ave

Draw a line to match each word to a picture.

bridge

brown

bread

brothers

bricks

cr sound

Write **cr** in the gaps to make these words.
Read them out.

___ ___y	___ ___ash
___ ___ew	___ ___isp
___ ___umb	___ ___unch
___ ___eak	___ ___eam
___ ___ate	___ ___ust

Look at the picture clues. Write the
letters **cr** in the correct place in the
crossword.

Across	Down
🦀	👑
✏️	🐊
✖️	

a b

a y o n

c

o s s

o

w

n

d

i

l

e

Note for parent: Ask your child to try to spell these sand other words containing the **cr** sound.
For example: crop, crow, crack, crane.

11

Sounds: **st, str, sp, sl, sw**

Say the sounds:

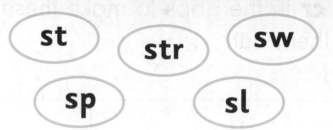

Say the name of each picture. Write the sound to match the picture.

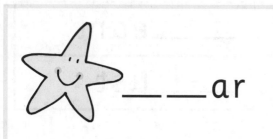 _____ ar

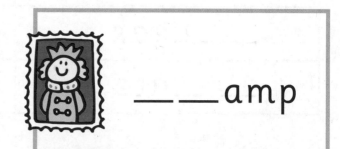 _____ amp

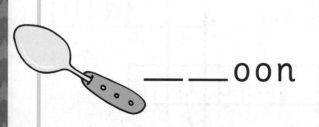 _____ oon

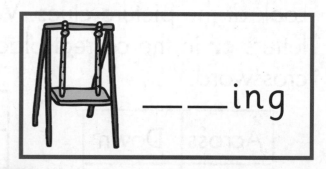 _____ ing

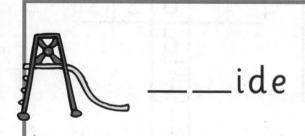 _____ ide

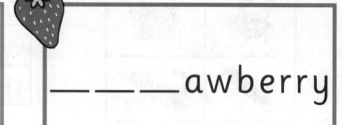 _____ awberry

Note for parent: Ask your child to look in a dictionary for more words beginning with these sounds.

th sound

First write **th** to make each word. LOOK at the word. COVER it up. WRITE it on the line below. CHECK if you are right!

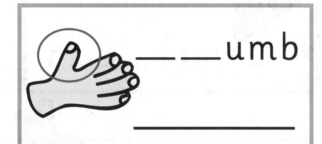 ___ ___umb

_____

 ___ ___istle

_____

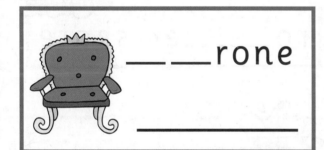 ___ ___rone

_____

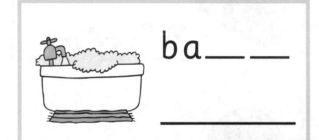 ba___ ___

_____

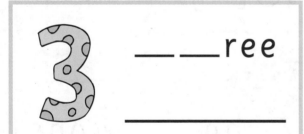 ___ ___ree

_____

too___ ___brush

_____

3+2 = 5
9-6 = 3

ma___ ___s

_____

Note for parent: Ask your child to look in a dictionary for more words beginning with this sound.

13

Double letters: ll

Say the name of each picture. Spell the word next to each picture.

 be____

 umbre____a

 wa____

 ro____er skate

 ba____

 ye____ow

 je____y

ba____oons

 caterpi____ars

Note for parent: Tell your child that in these words, double letters ll have a single vowel before them.

Double letters: oo

Say the name of each picture. Spell the word next to each picture.

 b __ __ k

 m __ __ n

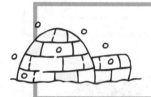 igl __ __

 sp __ __ n

 ball __ __ n

 kangar __ __ __

 d __ __ r

 t __ __ __ th

 h __ __ k

Note for parent: Tell your child that the double letters **oo** have different sounds in these words.

15

ow or ou?

Say what is in the picture. Write **ow** or **ou** to finish off the word.

c _ _ _

cl _ _ n

m _ _ _ se

h _ _ _ se

_ _ _ l

fl _ _ _ ers

rainb _ _ _

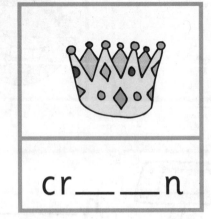

cr _ _ _ n

wind _ _ _

Choose a word to fill each gap.

goat

pear

feather

coat

boat

1. I felt sea sick on the _____.

2. I saw a _____ on the farm.

3. I put on my _____.

4. I can eat a _____.

5. I found a _____.

Note for parent: This activity introduces common vowel combinations that are used to create different sounds.

Say what is in the picture. Spell the word next to it.

__ai__

__ __ai__

__ __ai__ __ __

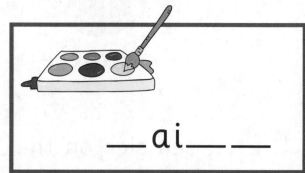

__ai__ __

__ai__

__ai__ __ __ __

Note for parent: Ask your child to try to spell these and other words containing the **ai** sound.
For example: chain, main, tail, nail, mail.

ee or ea?

Say what is in each picture.

Write each word on the correct list. Check your spellings in a dictionary.

ee	ea
cheese	

Note for parent: Tell your child that, in these words, the letters **ee** and **ea** sound the same.

19

Silent letters

Some words have silent letters. You see a silent letter in a word but you do not hear it when you say the word. Underline the letters that are silent in the words below.

knife   guitar   knight   wheel

comb   thumb   wrist   badge

gnome   knitting

Note for parent: Ask your child to try to spell these and other words containing silent letters.
For example: island, knee, limb, yacht.

Rhyming words

Draw lines to join the words that end with the same sounds.

Choose words from this list to complete the rhyme.

out	**sprout**	**spout**	**shout**
rain	**train**	**again**	

Incy Wincy Spider climbed up the water _____.

Down came the rain and washed the spider _____.

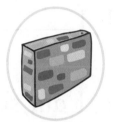

Out came the sunshine and dried up all the _____.

So Incy Wincy Spider climbed up the spout _____!

Note for parent: Ask your child to try to spell these rhyming words.

21

Everyday words

Copy the words from the box into the right sentences.

laugh	because	here
once	water	would

1. I _____ like a new bike.

2. I am staying indoors _____ it is raining.

3. My sister likes to make me _____ .

4. I _____ went to a football match.

5. I wash with _____ .

6. My house is _____ .

Note for parent: These common words are used frequently in the English language. It would be useful for your child to learn to spell them by heart.

Colours

LOOK at the word. COVER it up. WRITE it on the line. CHECK if you are right!

 blue _____

 pink _____

 green _____

 purple _____

 red _____

 black _____

 orange _____

 white _____

 yellow _____

 grey _____

 brown _____

Note for parent: These common words are used frequently in the English language. It would be useful for your child to learn to spell them by heart.

23

Days of the week

Finish these sentences.

Monday

On _____
I go swimming.

Tuesday

On _____
I play football.

Wednesday

On _____
I feed the ducks.

Thursday

On _____
I help Dad do the shopping.

Friday

On _____
I go to see my gran.

Saturday

On _____
I go to a party.

Sunday

On _____ I help Mum wash her car.

Note for parent: Remind your child that the days of the week begin with a capital letter.

Compound words

A compound word is made up of two short ones.
Write a word by each picture. Join two pictures
to make a compound word.

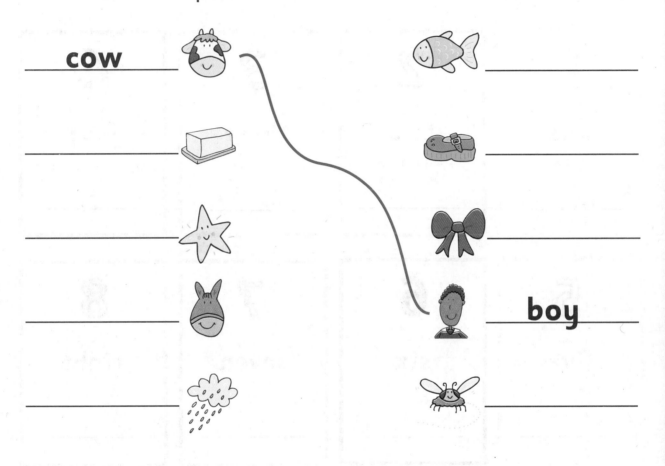

cow _____

_____

_____

_____

_____

_____ fish

_____

_____

_____ **boy**

_____

Now write your new words.

cowboy _____   _____

_____   _____

Note for parent: Ask your child to try to spell these and other compound words.
For example: tugboat, hairbrush, dustbin, bedroom, notebook.

25

LOOK at the word. COVER UP the word with your finger. WRITE the word on the line below. CHECK if you are right!

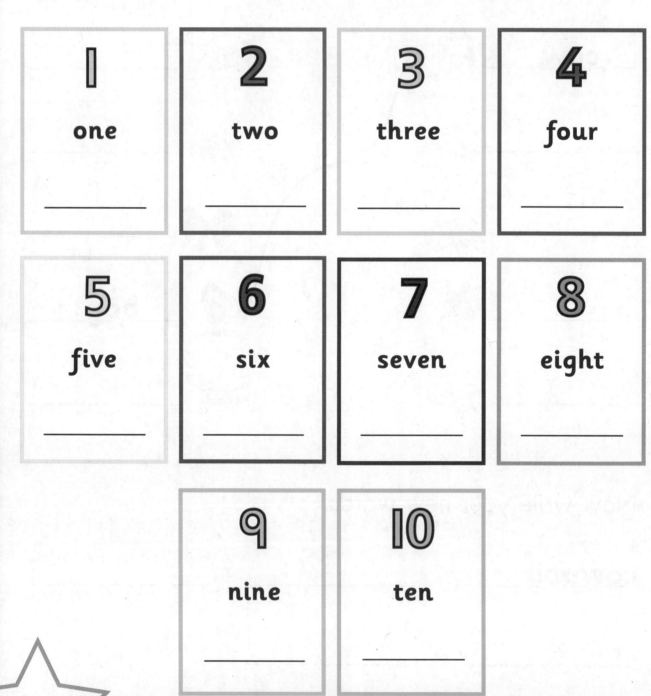

1 one ___	2 two ___	3 three ___	4 four ___
5 five ___	6 six ___	7 seven ___	8 eight ___
	9 nine ___	10 ten ___	

11 eleven ___	**12** twelve ___	**13** thirteen ___	**14** fourteen ___
15 fifteen ___	**16** sixteen ___	**17** seventeen ___	**18** eighteen ___
	19 nineteen ___	**20** twenty ___	

Note for parent: These common words are used frequently in the English language. Encourage your child to learn to spell them by heart.

Magic e

Add the letter **e** to a short word and magic happens. The vowel in the middle of the word changes its sound and the word changes its meaning.

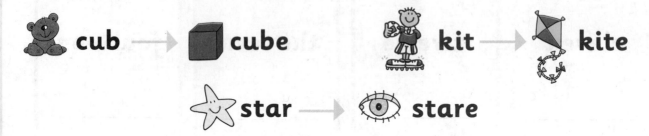

cub ⟶ cube   kit ⟶ kite

star ⟶ stare

Use magic **e** on these words.

cap ⟶ _ _ _ _   bit ⟶ _ _ _ _

hat ⟶ _ _ _ _   not ⟶ _ _ _ _

her ⟶ _ _ _ _   tub ⟶ _ _ _ _

The middles are missing from these words. Put the same missing letter in each pair of words, like this:

rid **and** ride

Choose from | a | e | i | o | u |

1. c__t **and** c__te   2. m__t **and** m__te

3. p__n **and** p__ne   4. h__p **and** h__pe

5. c__r **and** c__re   6. f__n **and** f__ne

Note for parent: Tell your child that when we add a final e to these words, the sound of the vowel changes from a hard (short) sound to a soft (long) sound.

More than one

Copy these words into the right boxes.

mouse	book	house
fox	cow	tooth
foxes	houses	cows
books	mice	teeth

One	More than one
mouse	mice
tooth	teeth

Note for parent: For most words we can add **-s**, **-es** or **-ies** to make the plural. But some words, such as 'mouse -> mice', change their spelling in more unusual ways.

Present and past

The present is something we are doing now. The past is something we have already done.

Present – I am painting a picture.

Past – I have painted a picture.

Add <u>ing</u> for the present and <u>ed</u> for the past.

Present	Past
wait_ _ _ _	wait_ _ _
jump_ _ _ _	jump_ _ _
sail_ _ _ _	sail_ _ _
walk_ _ _ _	walk_ _ _
talk_ _ _ _	talk_ _ _

Present	Past
crawl_ _ _ _	crawl_ _ _
climb_ _ _ _	climb_ _ _
wash_ _ _ _	wash_ _ _
brush_ _ _ _	brush_ _ _
laugh_ _ _ _	laugh_ _ _
cook_ _ _ _	cook_ _ _

Note for parent: This activity introduces the present and past tenses.

Tricky words

Some words are tricky to spell because they don't follow normal spelling patterns. Here are some of them.

anchor

pyjamas

biscuit

whistle

chef

penguin

saucer

Copy out any of these words you find hard to spell. Cover them up, then write them from memory. Keep going until you know the spelling.

_____   _____

_____   _____

_____   _____

_____   _____

Note for parent: Ask your child to use the LOOK, COVER, WRITE, CHECK method to learn to spell these words.

Answers

Pages 4-5 First letter sounds

egg ant cap dog goat hen box fish

1. ant 2. box 3. cap 4. dog
5. egg 6. fish 7. goat 8. hen

The king and queen had lots of pets.

They had a lion, a monkey and a pig.

They had an owl in a nest.

They had a rabbit with big ears.

They fed them all on jelly and ice cream.

1. ice cream 2. jelly 3. king 4. lion
5. monkey 6. nest 7. owl 8. pig
9. queen 10. rabbit

Page 6 First letter sounds

tap van wasp yellow zip umbrella
x-ray sun

1. sun 2. tap 3. umbrella 4. van
5. wasp 6. x-ray 7. yellow 8. zip

Page 7 Middle sounds

dog, cup, pig, bat, bed, wig, cat, fox,
web, duck, net, sun, rat, bus

Page 8 ch sound

chair, chick, cherry, children, chocolate,
cheese, church

Page 9 Wordsearch for sh

s	h	a	r	k	n	b
h	m	f	o	d	e	r
e	d	i	s	h	s	u
e	h	s	r	u	l	s
p	s	h	e	d	o	h

shark, brush, shed, sheep, dish, fish

Page 10 br sound

brain, branch, broom, bridle, brook,
bring, brim, breeze, bronze, brave

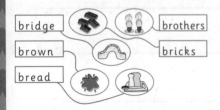

bridge brothers brown bricks bread

Page 11 cr sound

cry, crash,
crew, crisp,
crumb, crunch,
creak, cream,
crate, crust

			c	r	a	b
			r			
c	r	a	y	o	n	
r				c		
o		c	r	o	s	s
w				d		
n				i		
				l		
				e		

Page 12 Sounds: st, str, sp, sl, sw

star, stamp, spoon, swing, slide,
strawberry

Page 13 th sound

thumb, thistle, throne, bath, three,
toothbrush, maths

Page 14 Double letters: ll

bell, umbrella, wall, roller skate, ball,
yellow, jelly, balloons, caterpillars

Page 15 Double letters: oo

book, moon, igloo, spoon, balloon,
kangaroo, door, tooth, hook

Page 16 ow or ou?

cow, clown, mouse, house, owl, flowers,
rainbow, crown, window

Page 17 Middle sounds: oa and ea

1. I felt sea sick on the boat.
2. I saw a goat on the farm.
3. I put on my coat.
4. I can eat a pear.
5. I found a feather.

Page 18 Middle sound: ai

rain, train, trainer, paint, hair, rainbow

Page 19 ee or ea?

ee	ea
cheese	ice cream
queen	leaf
wheel	
tree	

Page 20 Silent letters

knife, guitar, knight, wheel, comb, thumb,
wrist, badge, gnome, knitting

Page 21 Rhyming words

Incy Wincy Spider climbed up the water
spout.

Down came the rain and washed the
spider out.

Out came the sunshine and dried up all
the rain.

So Incy Wincy Spider climbed up the
spout again.

Page 22 Everyday words

1. would 2. because 3. laugh
4. once 5. water 6. here

Page 24 Days of the week

On Monday I go swimming.

On Tuesday I play football.

On Wednesday I feed the ducks.

On Thursday I help Dad do the shopping.

On Friday I go to see my gran.

On Saturday I go to a party.

On Sunday I help Mum wash her car.

Page 25 Compound words

cow+boy = cowboy, butter+fly = butterfly,
star+fish = starfish, horse+shoe =
horseshoe, rain+bow = rainbow

Page 28 Magic e

cap–cape, bit–bite, hat–hate, not–note,
her–here, tub–tube

1. cut and cute 2. mat and mate
3. pin and pine 4. hop and hope
5. car and care 6. fin and fine

Page 29 More than one

One: mouse, book, house, fox, cow, tooth

More than one: mice, books, houses,
foxes, cows, teeth

Page 30 Present and past

Present	Past
waiting	waited
jumping	jumped
sailing	sailed
walking	walked
talking	talked
crawling	crawled
climbing	climbed
washing	washed
brushing	brushed
laughing	laughed
cooking	cooked